The world is full of possibilities, and so is your child!

HI PARENTS!

Keep the fun and learning going with this checklist of free learn-at-home resources!

☐ **PBS KIDS VIDEO APP**
available on mobile, tablet and connected TV devices and offers on-demand full episodes and more. No subscription required.

☐ **PBS KIDS GAMES APP**
offers nearly 200 educational games, which can be downloaded for offline play anytime, anywhere.

☐ **PBS KIDS 24/7 CHANNEL**
anytime access to educational series, including PBS KIDS Family Night every weekend (check local listings or livestream on the PBS KIDS Video app).

☐ **PBS KIDS for Parents**
tips, resources, and an Activity Finder where you can find learning activities based on your child's age, favorite show or topic. Visit pbskidsforparents.org.

ACTIVITY BOOK

Includes Geography, Math, and More!

Bendon, Inc. All rights reserved.
Ashland, OH 44805.

9 STORY™
MEDIA GROUP

In Carmen's home town of Mexico City,
she is asked to perform at the Day of the Dead festival.

The Day of the Dead is a holiday celebrated throughout Mexico where people gather to remember their loved ones. Help Carmen get ready for the celebration by finding and circling these items!

candy skull

sign

flowers

garland

Mexico is a country in North America.

Trace Mexico.

Mexico

Practice printing Mexico.

Fun Fact
Mexico City, the capital of Mexico, is one of the largest cities in the world. More than 20 million people live in and around the city.

Which garland of papel picado is different?

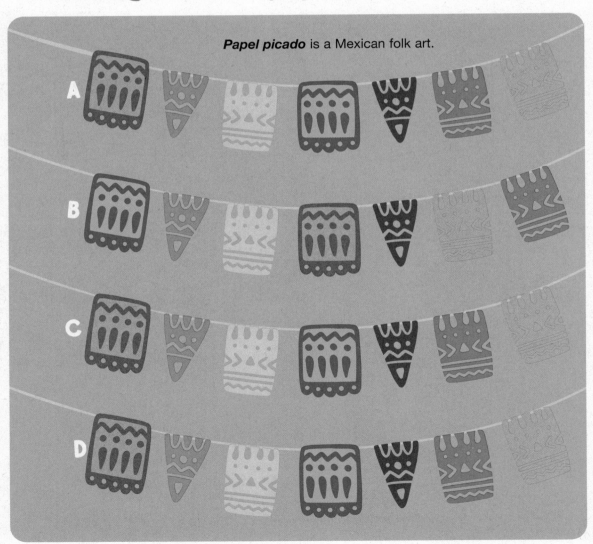

Papel picado is a Mexican folk art.

Make a Garland
Color your very own garland of papel picado!
Ask an adult to help you carefully cut along the dotted line.
Then tape them to string and hang it on the wall or furniture.

Make a Mask

This page is for the other side of
your garland of papel picado! Ask an adult to help you
carefully cut along the dotted line on the previous page.

Mariachi music is important to Mexico's celebrations and dance, and is one way to express the feelings and identity of the people and country. What are some things that are important in your family's celebrations? Write about them and draw a picture.

Luna and the gang are seeing the sights in Mexico City while Circo Fabuloso is performing there. Help them out by finding and circling these items!

Mexican Flag

The Angel of Independence statue

Circo Fabuloso sign

5 red flags

Numbers 1 to 10
Count the objects in each row.
Write the matching number next to each group of objects.

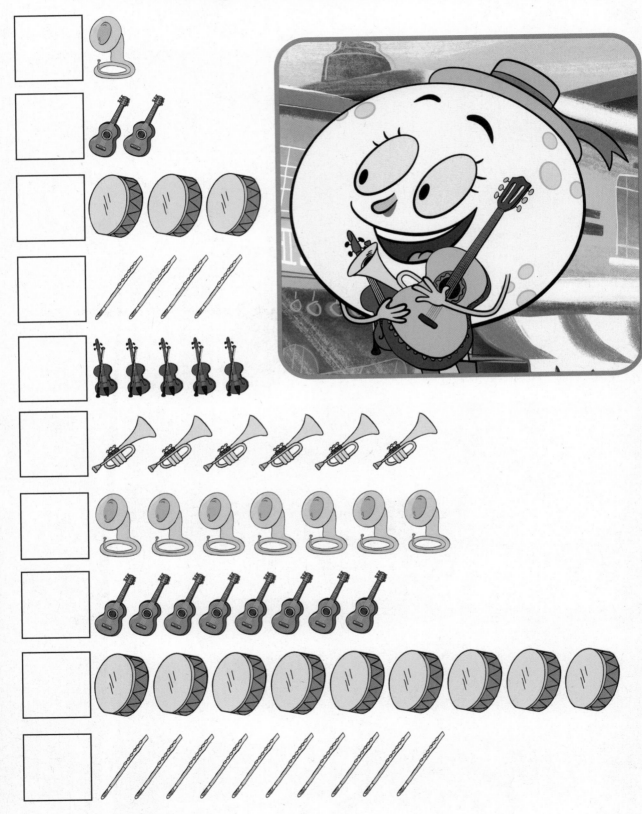

Murals are big paintings on walls.
In Mexico City, murals convey a sense of community, history, and culture.

In Mexico City, Andy wants to find a big surface to paint on, and he comes across some amazing murals! Help Andy by finding and circling these items!

Zócalo, the Plaza de la Constitución

trumpeter

the sun

ice cream cart

Create a Mural
Use this space to design your own mural.
What does your mural represent to you?

Adding Objects

Count the objects in each row.
Circle the same number of
things in each box.

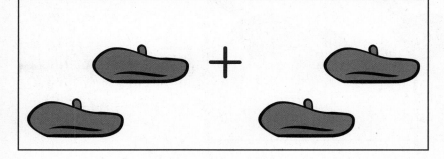

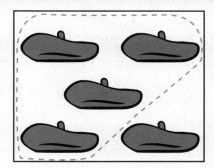

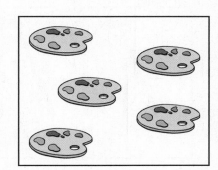

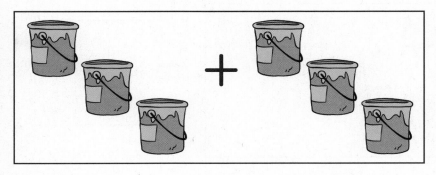

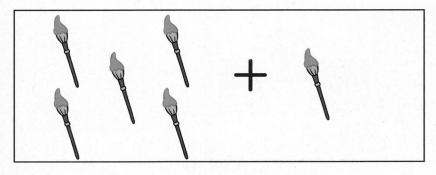

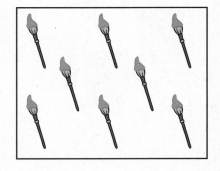

Subtracting Objects

Cross out objects to
subtract the correct number.
Write the difference in each box.

5 - 1 =

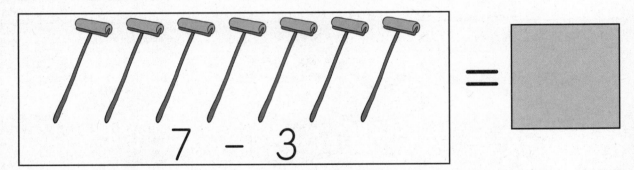

7 - 3 =

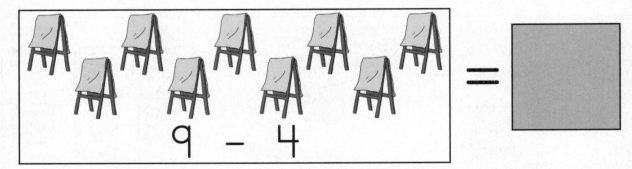

9 - 4 =

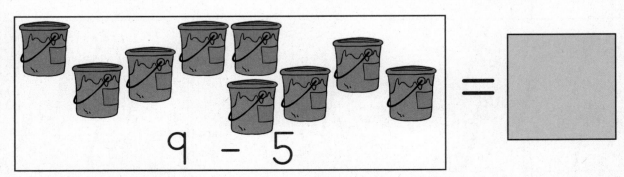

9 - 5 =

Leo, Andy, and Carmen decide to give Luna her own special day.
They travel to China, which already celebrates her with the Moon Festival.

Design a Lantern

If you were making a lantern for the Moon Festival,
what would it look like? Draw a picture of it in the space below.

Write the Sum

When you add two groups together the answer is called the sum. Count the objects in each group and add them together!

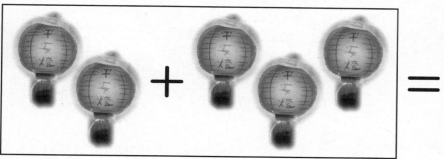

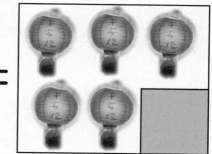

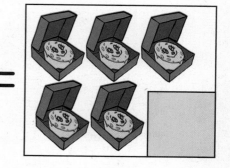

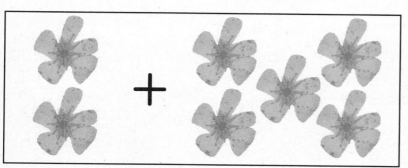

The Forbidden City in Beijing, contains the former imperial palaces. Long ago, entry was forbidden to all except the imperial family and staff. Now, help Luna and the gang explore by finding and circling these items!

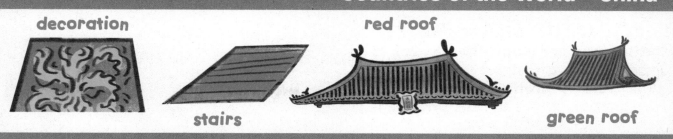

decoration

stairs

red roof

green roof

Write the Differences

When you subtract, the answer is called the difference. Cross out objects to subtract the correct number. Write the difference in each box.

4 - 1
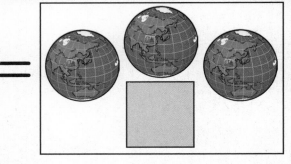

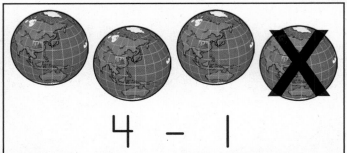
6 - 2
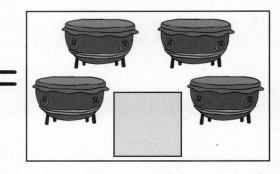

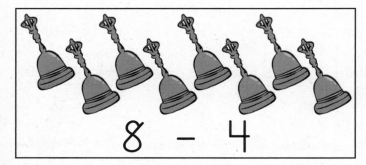
8 - 4

8 - 5

Chopsticks are the traditional utensil for eating food in China.
Leo is learning that patience is an important part of practicing anything new.

Food is an important part of Chinese culture and has influenced many other cuisines all over Asia. Circle these items around the restaurant where Leo learned how to use chopsticks!

baby panda

2 plates of food

chopsticks

cash register

Was there a time when you learned a new skill?
Did you have to practice a lot? Write about it in the space below.
Draw a picture of yourself practicing your new skill.

China is a country in Asia.

Trace China.

Fun Fact
The Great Wall of China is the longest structure ever built.
It is one of the Wonders of the Ancient World.

Practice printing China.

Color the Great Wall of China.

Countries of the World - China

Follow the Path
Using the pattern below,
follow the correct path
through the maze.

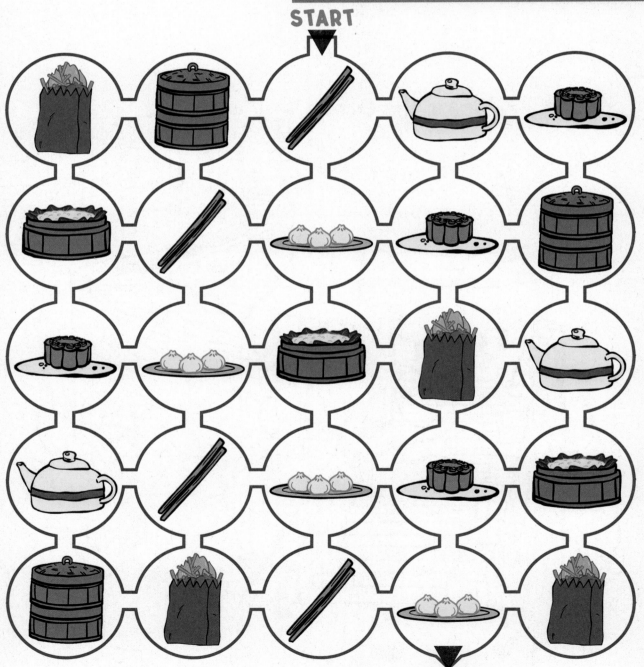

Luna and her friends visit London, England, which has many human-made features, such as streets, buildings, statues, and bridges. London has a famous landmark called Big Ben.

Tower Bridge is another famous landmark in London. It is a bridge with a drawbridge in the middle that can be swung upward. Help Luna and the gang enjoy their ride on the River Thames by finding and circling these items!

side bridge tower

drawbridge

crown detail

boat

Connect-the-Dots
Draw a line from dot to dot, in numerical order, to finish the picture!

United Kingdom is a country in Europe.

Trace United Kingdom.

United Kingdom

Practice printing United Kingdom.

Fun Fact
The United Kingdom is made up of four countries under one government: England, Scotland, Wales, and Northern Ireland.

The United Kingdom is under a constitutional monarchy rule (they have kings and queens).

How many crowns do you count?

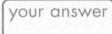

your answer

Design a Landmark
Design your own person-made feature, also called a landmark.
It could be a street, a building, a statue, or a bridge.
Draw in the space below.

Telling Time

A clock has two hands. The short hand is the **hour** hand. The long hand is the **minute** hand.

Look at the hands of the clock. Color the hour hand **purple**. Color the minute hand **blue**.

When the hour hand points to the 12, we say o'clock.

The **hour** hand is on the 4 and the **minute** hand is on the 12. It is 4 o'clock. We can also write the time as four o'clock or 4:00.

Look at the clock next to each picture. Circle the correct time.

1.

A. 3 o'clock   B. 2 o'clock

2.

A. 12 o'clock   B. 6 o'clock

3.

A. 8 o'clock   B. 1 o'clock

4.

A. 9 o'clock   B. 5 o'clock

Telling Time

When the minute hand points to the 6,
it is halfway around the clock.
We say it is **half past the hour**.

30 minutes equals
half of an hour.
Half past 12 or 12:30

Look at the clocks below. Read the **hour** hand first,
then read the **minute** hand. Write the correct time.

1.

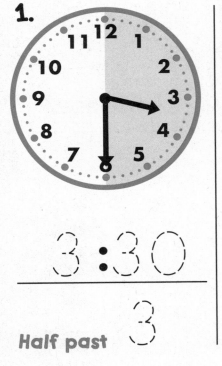

3 : 30

Half past 3

2.

:

Half past

3.

:

Half past

Russia has long, cold winters and unique traditional clothes for keeping warm. Luna's friend Nikolai takes the kids on his troika (sled) to get some.

Circo Fabuloso gets snowed in by an ice storm in Moscow. Moscow is the most densely populated city and the capital of Russia. Help Luna and the gang keep warm by finding and circling these items!

Russian Flag

onion dome

arched window

dark green roof

Weather Outfitter
What is the temperature like where you live?
What kind of clothes do you wear for the weather?
Draw a picture of them in the space below.

Russia is a country mainly in Asia, though parts are in Europe.

Trace Russia.

Russia

Practice printing Russia.

Fun Fact
Russia has the largest land area of any country in the world. The capital of Russia is Moscow.

WORD SEARCH

Czar   Kremlin   Moscow
ballet   Siberia   Volga River
bear   Sputnik   Tetris

For answers, see page 34.

```
D  H  Z  S  I  B  E  R  I  A
V  A  B  A  D  V  E  T  S  C
Q  D  A  J  M  O  U  A  G  Z
R  M  L  P  L  K  A  H  R  A
V  O  L  G  A  R  I  V  E  R
E  S  E  H  R  E  O  M  U  S
J  C  T  N  G  M  F  K  R  C
A  O  I  W  E  L  D  S  O  Z
N  W  E  B  S  I  R  T  E  T
F  S  P  U  T  N  I  K  E  G
```

Telling the Weather

It is easy to tell what weather it is outside when you are there. You can feel the temperature and see how bright the sun is. How can you tell the weather when you are not there, like in a picture? Through observation, or carefully looking, you can find clues on the weather where the picture takes place. Can you see the sun? Are the people wearing summer clothes? It could be hot. Is there snow? Are the people wearing winter clothes? It could be cold. Cool, warm, chilly, burning, crisp, and frosty can also describe temperatures of weather.

The weather in this picture looks cold!

The weather in this picture looks hot!

Look at the picture and circle the closest weather that matches the picture.

1.

A. Hot   **B. Cold**

2.

A. Hot   **B. Cold**

3.

A. Hot   **B. Cold**

4.

A. Hot   **B. Cold**

Telling More Weather

Hot and cold describe temperatures of weather, but there are more aspects to weather. Sunny, rainy, snowy, cloudy, icy, windy, stormy, and foggy also describe the state of atmospheric weather.

How's the weather where you are?

Look at the picture and circle the closest weather that matches the picture.

1.

A. Rainy   **B. Snowy**

2.

A. Cool   **B. Stormy**

3.

A. Cloudy   **B. Sunny**

4.

A. Rainy   **B. Icy**

5.

A. Sunny   **B. Foggy**

6.

A. Stormy   **B. Summery**

The World. Our planet is also called Earth.

Check out where *Luna* and the gang visited in this book, then color the oceans blue!

**London, England
United Kingdom**

Moscow, Russia

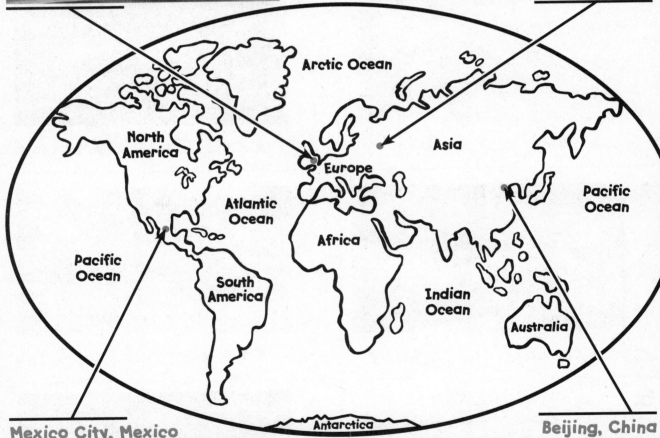

Arctic Ocean

North
America

Europe

Asia

Pacific
Ocean

Atlantic
Ocean

Africa

Pacific
Ocean

South
America

Indian
Ocean

Australia

Antarctica

Mexico City, Mexico

Beijing, China

Page 4-5

Page 10-11

Page 12

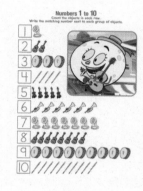

Page 14-15

Page 17

Page 18

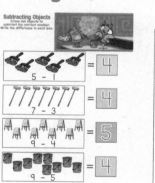

Page 21

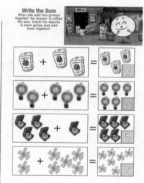

Page 22-23

Page 24

Answer Key

Page 26-27

Food is an important part of Chinese culture and has influenced many other cuisines all over Asia. Circle these items around the restaurant where Leo learned how to use chopsticks!

baby panda   chopsticks

2 plates of food   cash register

Page 30

Follow the Path
Using the pattern below, follow the correct path through the maze.

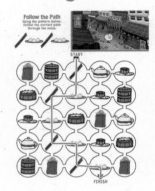

Page 32-33

Tower Bridge is another famous landmark in London. It is a bridge with a drawbridge in the middle that can be swung upward. Help Luna and the gang enjoy their ride on the River Thames by finding and circling these items!

side bridge tower   crown detail

drawbridge   boat

Page 34

Connect-the-Dots
Draw a line from dot to dot, in numerical order, to finish the picture!

Page 37

Telling Time
A clock has two hands. The short hand is the hour hand. The long hand is the minute hand.

Look at the hands of the clock. Color the hour hand purple. Color the minute hand blue.

When the hour hand points to the 12, we say o'clock.

The hour hand is on the 4 and the minute hand is to the 12. It is 4 o'clock. We can also write the time as four o'clock or 4:00.

Look at the clock next to each picture. Circle the correct time.

1. A. 3 o'clock   B. 2 o'clock
2. A. 12 o'clock   B. 6 o'clock
3. A. 8 o'clock   B. 1 o'clock
4. A. 4 o'clock   B. 5 o'clock

Page 38

Telling Time
When the minute hand points to the 6, it is halfway around the clock. We say it is half past the hour.

60 minutes equals half of an hour.
Half past 12 or 12:30

Look at the clocks below. Read the hour hand first, then read the minute hand. Write the correct time.

1. **3:30** half past **3**
2. **1:30** half past **1**
3. **9:30** half past **9**

Page 40-41

Circo Fabuloso gets snowed in by an ice storm in Moscow. Moscow is the most densely populated city and the capital of Russia. Help Luna and the gang keep warm by finding and circling these items!

Russian flag   arched window

onion detail   dark green roof

Page 43

Russia is a country mainly in Asia, though parts are in Europe.

Trace Russia.
Russia

Practice printing Russia.

Fun Fact
Russia has the largest land area of any country in the world.
The capital of Russia is Moscow.

WORD SEARCH
Czar   Kremlin   Moscow
tsar   Siberia   Volga River
bear   Sputnik   Tsina

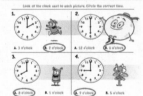

Page 44

Telling the Weather
It is easy to tell what weather it is outside when you are there. You can feel the temperature and see how bright the sun is. How can you tell the weather when you are not there, like in a picture? Through observation, or carefully looking, you can find clues to the weather where the picture takes place.

Can you see the sun? Are the people wearing summer clothes? It could be hot, warm, sunny, or humid. Is there snow? Are the people wearing winter clothes? It could be cold. Cool, warm, chilly, burning, crisp, and frosty are also words that describe temperatures of weather.

The weather in this picture looks cold!

The weather in this picture looks hot!

Look at the picture and circle the closest weather that matches the picture.

1. A. Hot   B. Cold
2. A. Hot   B. Cold
3. A. Hot   B. Cold
4. A. Hot   B. Cold

Page 45

Telling More Weather
Hot and cold describe temperatures of weather, but there are more words to weather. Sunny, rainy, snowy, cloudy, icy, windy, stormy, and foggy also describe the state of atmospheric weather.

How's the weather where you are?

Look at the picture and circle the closest weather that matches the picture.

1. A. Rainy   B. Sunny
2. A. Cold   B. Stormy
3. A. Cloudy   B. Sunny
4. A. Rainy   B. Icy
5. A. Sunny   B. Foggy
6. A. Stormy   B. Summery